Little Bo-peep

and friends

Miles Kelly

First published in 2011 by Miles Kelly Publishing Ltd
Harding's Barn, Bardfield End Green, Thaxted, Essex, CM6 3PX, UK

This edition printed in 2013

4 6 8 10 9 7 5

Editorial Director Belinda Gallagher

Art Director Jo Cowan

Editor Sarah Parkin

Cover/Junior Designer Kayleigh Allen

Production Manager Elizabeth Collins

Reprographics Stephan Davis, Ian Paulyn

Assets Lorraine King

ISBN 978-1-84810-415-0

Printed in China

British Library Cataloguing-in-Publication Data
A catalogue record for this book is available from the British Library

ACKNOWLEDGEMENTS

Artworks are from the Miles Kelly Artwork Bank
Cover artist: Kirsten Wilson

Made with paper from a sustainable forest

www.mileskelly.net
info@mileskelly.net
www.factsforprojects.com

Contents

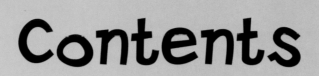

Oranges and Lemons

Oranges and lemons,
Say the bells of St Clement's.

You owe me five farthings,
Say the bells of St Martin's.

When will you pay me?
Say the bells of Old Bailey.

Two children representing oranges and lemons form an arch.

The other children pass beneath.

On the final verse, the arch falls and the child beneath chooses to stand behind 'oranges' or 'lemons'.

When I grow rich,
Say the bells of Shoreditch.

When will that be?
Say the bells of Stepney.

I do not know,
Says the great bell of Bow.

Here comes a candle
To light you to bed.

Here comes a chopper
To chop off your head!

Mix a Pancake

Mix a pancake,
Stir a pancake,
Pop it in the pan;
Fry the pancake,
Toss the pancake —
Catch it if you can.

Christina Rossetti
1830–94, b. England

If you're Happy and you Know it

If you're happy and you know it,
clap your hands.
If you're happy and you know it,
clap your hands.
If you're happy and you know it
and you really want to show it,
If you're happy and you know it
clap your hands.

Repeat the words again, but change the action to stamping your feet, clicking your fingers and touching your head.

Goosey, Goosey Gander

Goosey, goosey gander,
Whither shall I wander?
Upstairs and downstairs
And in my lady's chamber.

There I met an old man
Who would not say his prayers,
I took him by his left leg
And threw him down the stairs.

Snow White and Rose Red

A retelling from the original story
by the Brothers Grimm

Once upon a time there was a widow who had two daughters, Snow White and Rose Red. Snow White was quiet and gentle, Rose Red was wild as the hills, but they loved each other, and their mother, so the house in the woods was a happy one.

One winter evening there was a knock at the door. Rose Red opened it and gave a scream. There stood a great big brown bear! But in a deep rumbly voice the bear said, "Please do not be afraid. All I ask is that you let me sleep by your fire tonight. It is so cold outside."

"Of course you may shelter with us," said the mother. She called the girls to set the soup on the stove and to put another log on the fire.

"Would you brush the snow from my fur, please?" asked the bear. Rose Red fetched the big broom and carefully brushed the bear's shaggy coat. Snow White gave him a great bowl of hot soup and the bear gulped it down in one. Then he stretched out in front of the fire and was soon fast asleep.

In the morning, Snow White let him out of the cottage. He padded off into the forest through the deep snow. In the evening, he returned

and once again Snow White and Rose Red and their mother looked after him. The bear came every night all through the winter, and they grew very fond of him. But when spring came, the bear told them he would not be returning any more.

"I have to guard my treasure. Once the snows have melted all kinds of wicked people try to steal it," he said, and giving them all a hug, he set off through the forest. Just as he passed through the garden gate, his fur caught on a nail. For a moment Snow White thought she saw a glint of gold, but the bear hurried off and was soon out of sight.

A few days later, Rose Red and Snow White were out gathering berries when they came alongside a fallen tree. They saw a very cross dwarf, tugging at his beard, which was trapped by the great tree trunk.

"Well, don't stand there like a pair of silly geese! Come and help me!" he shrieked.

No matter how hard they tugged, Rose Red and Snow White were not strong enough to lift the tree, so Rose Red took her scissors out and snipped off the end of the dwarf's beard. He was furious, and snatched up a big bag of gold from the tree roots and disappeared without a word of thanks.

Some days later the girls' mother said she fancied a piece of fish for supper, so they went down to the river to see what they could catch. There on the bank they found the cross dwarf again. This time his beard was caught up in his fishing line.

"Don't just stand there gawping," he yelled, "help me get free!"

Snow White tried to untangle it but it was impossible, so she too snipped a piece off his beard. He was white with rage, but just grasped a casket of jewels that lay at the water's edge and turned away without a word of thanks.

It was the Spring Fair a few days later. The girls decided to go and buy some new ribbons for their hats, and their mother wanted needles for her embroidery. They had not gone far when they heard a terrible shrieking. Snow White and Rose Red ran towards the sound, and there was the cross dwarf, this time struggling in the talons of an eagle. The girls tugged and tugged and the eagle had to let go.

"You have torn my coat," muttered the ungrateful dwarf and picked up a basket of pearls and hobbled off as fast as possible. The girls laughed and continued on their way to the fair.

They had a wonderful time, and it was late when they walked home. The sun was just sinking behind a big rock when, to their astonishment, they came across the dwarf again. There, spread out on the ground in front of him, was a great pile of gold, precious jewels and pearls.

Suddenly the dwarf saw Snow White and Rose Red.

"Go away! Go away! You horrid girls are always in my way," he shouted. But then there was a huge growl and the great bear stood by their side. With one huge paw he swiped the dwarf up, up into the sky and no one ever saw where he fell to earth again. The bear turned towards Snow White and Rose Red and as they looked, his shaggy coat fell away. There stood a handsome young man, dressed in a golden suit.

"Do not be afraid, Snow White and

Rose Red," he said smiling. "Now you can see who I really am. That wicked dwarf put a spell on me so he could steal all my treasure, but you have broken the spell by your kindness."

They all went home with the treasure. They talked long into the night, and it was all still true the next morning! Snow White married the handsome young man who, by great good fortune, had a younger brother who married Rose Red, and they all lived happily ever after.

So if you ever find a dwarf with half his beard missing, be very careful.

Little Bo-peep

Little Bo-peep
has lost her sheep,
And can't tell where
to find them;
Leave them alone,
and they'll come home,
Bringing their tails
behind them.

One, Two, Three, Four, Five

One, two, three, four, five,
Once I caught a fish alive.
Six, seven, eight, nine, ten,
Then I let it go again.

Why did you let it go?
Because it bit my finger so.
Which finger did it bite?
This little finger on the right.

The Old Woman who Lived in a Shoe

There was an old woman
who lived in a shoe,
She had so many children
she didn't know what to do.

She gave them some broth
without any bread;
She whipped them all soundly
and put them to bed.

Ring-a-ring o' Roses

All hold hands and skip around in a ring.

On the last line all sit down on the ground and repeat.

Ring-a-ring o'rc
A pocket full of posies,
A-tishoo! A-tishoo!
We all fall down.

Hot-cross Buns

Hot-cross buns!
Hot-cross buns!
One a penny, two a penny,
Hot-cross buns!

Hot-cross buns!
Hot-cross buns!
If you have no daughters
Give them to your sons.

Dick Whittington and his Cat

An English myth

Hundreds of years ago there lived a poor boy called Dick Whittington. His only possession was his cat, but everyone in his village looked after him. In return, he worked hard wherever he was needed. Dick's greatest dream was to visit London, where he had heard the streets were paved with gold.

One day, a waggoner pulled into the village. Dick offered to rub the horses down, and was soon telling the waggoner all about his dreams of visiting London.

"Well, you must be in luck today," smiled

the waggoner, "for that is where I am bound. Why don't you come with me and I will drop you off back here again on my return tomorrow?"

So Dick and his cat waved goodbye to the villagers and set off with the waggoner for London. When they arrived, Dick looked round in astonishment. Never before had he seen such huge buildings, all crowded so closely together. And there were so many people! Dick set off to explore, promising the waggoner he would be back in the evening.

The pavements certainly did not appear to be paved with gold. But Dick kept on thinking he should just try round the next corner.

Before long, Dick realized that he was lost. He stumbled into a doorway, and worn out with hunger and worry, he fell asleep.

Dick had chosen a good doorway to sleep in. The house belonged to a rich merchant, Mr Fitzwarren, who was willing to help anyone in need. So when he came home later that evening, Mr Fitzwarren took Dick and his cat indoors and told the cook to give him supper. The cook was very grumpy at having to prepare a meal for Dick because she thought he looked like a ragamuffin.

The next day, Mr Fitzwarren told Dick that the streets of London were not paved with gold, and that life there was hard.

"But you look like a strong boy, would you like to work for me?" he asked. "You will have a roof over your head and a good dinner every day in return for helping in the kitchen and the stables."

Dick was delighted and soon settled into the household. He worked hard and everyone liked him, except the cook. She gave him all the horrible jobs in the kitchen. But she didn't dare defy her master so Dick had a good dinner every day.

Whenever one of Mr Fitzwarren's ships went to sea, it was custom for everyone in the household to give something to the ship's cargo for luck. Dick had only his cat. He sadly handed her over.

The ship was at sea for many months before they came to port in China. The captain and crew went ashore to show the emperor their cargo. The emperor had known the captain for years and they were old friends, so they sat down to a banquet. But to the emperor's embarrassment, the meal was ruined by the rats that ran everywhere. The emperor explained that they had tried everything but nothing could rid the court of the plague of rats. The captain smiled.

"I think I have the answer," he said and he sent for Dick's cat. Within moments of her arrival, there were piles of dead rats. He was so impressed that he gave the captain a ship filled of gold.

Back in London, Dick's life was a misery. The cook was nastier than ever and he didn't even have his beloved cat for company, so one day he ran away. He had not gone far before he heard the church bells ringing, and they seemed to say,

"Turn again Dick Whittington,
Thrice Lord Mayor of London."

Dick didn't know what the bells meant,

but he remembered how kind Mr Fitzwarren had been, so he turned around and went back. When the ships came home, Mr Fitzwarren gave Dick his fair share and more. This was the start of Dick's prosperity, and he even married Mr Fitzwarren's daughter, Jane. He did become Lord Mayor of London three times, but he never forgot his early days of poverty and he founded schools and hospitals for the poor. He and Jane had many children, and there were always lots of cats in their great house as well!

The Little Turtle

There was a little turtle,
He lived in a box.
He swam in a puddle,
He climbed on the rocks.

He snapped at a mosquito,
He snapped at a flea.
He snapped at a minnow,
And he snapped at me.

He caught the mosquito,
He caught the flea.
He caught the minnow,
But he didn't catch me.

Vachel Lindsay
1879–1931, b. USA

I'm a Little Teapot

I'm a little teapot,
Short and stout,
Here's my handle,
Here's my spout.
When I see the teacups,
Hear me shout,
"Tip me up, and pour me out!"

Place one hand on your hip to be the handle.

Place the opposite arm out to the side to be the spout.

On the final line, lean over to the side to pour the tea.

37

Twinkle, Twinkle, Little Star

Twinkle, twinkle, little star,
How I wonder what you are.
Up above the world so high,
Like a diamond in the sky.

When the blazing sun is gone,
When he nothing shines upon,
Then you show your little light,
Twinkle, twinkle, all the night.

Mary, Mary

Mary, Mary, quite contrary,
How does your garden grow?
With silver bells and cockle shells,
And pretty maids all in a row.